PRAISE FOR
BIG GORGEOUS JAZZ MACHINE

"These works—that are a delight to the eye and a dream for the ear—are exactly what I look for in poetry comics. They experiment with visions of text (and absence of text) and our human greed for narrative. 'A house operates within the house autonomously.' Potter writes. 'A psychological diagram emerges.' This is what is happening in this impressive collection, a psychological map arises in blobs of bright colors, scratches of pencil, and little mutable batches of text for us to examine. These comics are adorable, poignant, elegant, humorous, strange and tragic: like I said, everything I want."

– Bianca Stone, author of *The Möbius Strip Club of Grief*

"A lovely collection of poetry comics that don't fear the page, the materials, or the reader. Every piece pushes a little deeper than you can anticipate, and every page shows off a fresh new experiment. Considered, organic, delectable!"

– Sam Alden, author of *New Construction*

"What is a feeling? What is a poem? What is silence? What is a word? I used to have answers to these questions. Then I read Nick Potter's *Big Gorgeous Jazz Machine.* Now I only have ecstatic fever dreams of blobs and swirls stretching and oozing, folding and swelling across an open field of limitless possibilities. This is an amazing book, and you will love it!"

– Kathryn Nuernberger, author of *The Witch of Eye*

"A beguiling and beautiful collection of comics that seem to grow from the page, capturing fleeting moments with organic grace."

– Simon Moreton, author of *Where?*

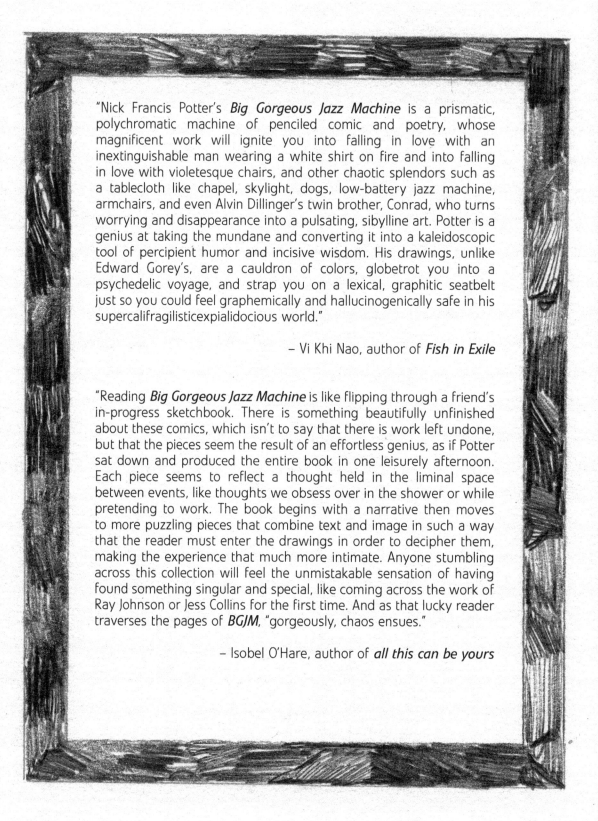

"Nick Francis Potter's *Big Gorgeous Jazz Machine* is a prismatic, polychromatic machine of penciled comic and poetry, whose magnificent work will ignite you into falling in love with an inextinguishable man wearing a white shirt on fire and into falling in love with violetesque chairs, and other chaotic splendors such as a tablecloth like chapel, skylight, dogs, low-battery jazz machine, armchairs, and even Alvin Dillinger's twin brother, Conrad, who turns worrying and disappearance into a pulsating, sibylline art. Potter is a genius at taking the mundane and converting it into a kaleidoscopic tool of percipient humor and incisive wisdom. His drawings, unlike Edward Gorey's, are a cauldron of colors, globetrot you into a psychedelic voyage, and strap you on a lexical, graphitic seatbelt just so you could feel graphemically and hallucinogenically safe in his supercalifragilisticexpialidocious world."

– Vi Khi Nao, author of *Fish in Exile*

"Reading *Big Gorgeous Jazz Machine* is like flipping through a friend's in-progress sketchbook. There is something beautifully unfinished about these comics, which isn't to say that there is work left undone, but that the pieces seem the result of an effortless genius, as if Potter sat down and produced the entire book in one leisurely afternoon. Each piece seems to reflect a thought held in the liminal space between events, like thoughts we obsess over in the shower or while pretending to work. The book begins with a narrative then moves to more puzzling pieces that combine text and image in such a way that the reader must enter the drawings in order to decipher them, making the experience that much more intimate. Anyone stumbling across this collection will feel the unmistakable sensation of having found something singular and special, like coming across the work of Ray Johnson or Jess Collins for the first time. And as that lucky reader traverses the pages of *BGJM*, "gorgeously, chaos ensues."

– Isobel O'Hare, author of *all this can be yours*

DRIFTWOOD PRESS

BIG
GORGEOUS
JAZZ
MACHINE

COMICS/POEMS

NICK FRANCIS POTTER

Independently published by Driftwood Press
in the United States of America.

Comic Editors & Interviewers:
James McNulty & Jerrod Schwarz

Cover Design:
Nick Francis Potter & Sally Franckowiak

Interior Design & Copyeditor:
James McNulty

First published: March 22nd, 2022
ISBN-13: 978-1949065145

Please visit our website at www.driftwoodpress.net
or email us at editor@driftwoodpress.net.

"MUSIC IS LIQUID COMICS;
COMICS ARE FROZEN MUSIC."
- GOETHE

"A COMICS PANEL THAT HAS BEEN
EXPERIENCED IS NOT AN INERT BOX.
INHABITED COMICS TRANSCEND
GEOMETRICAL SPACE."
- BACHELARD

PROLOGUE

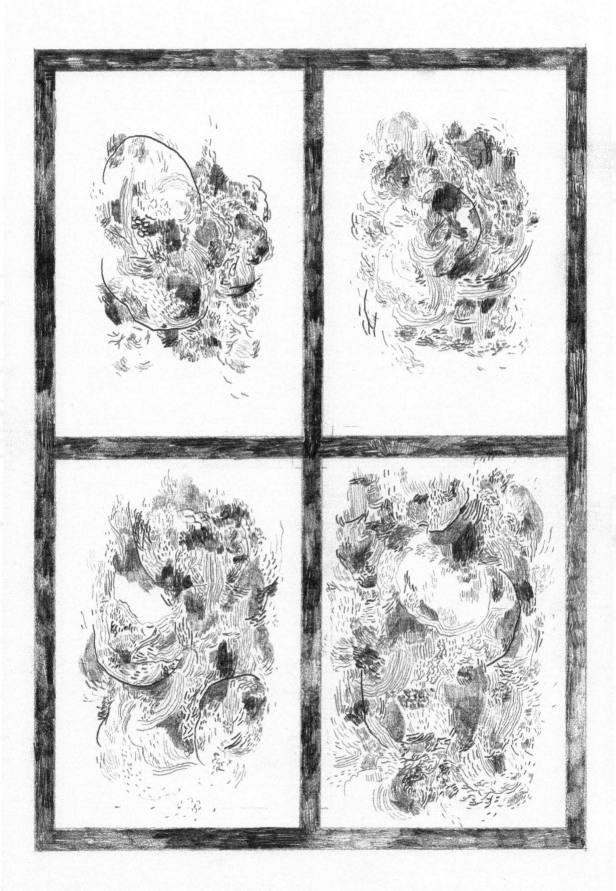

VACATIONING

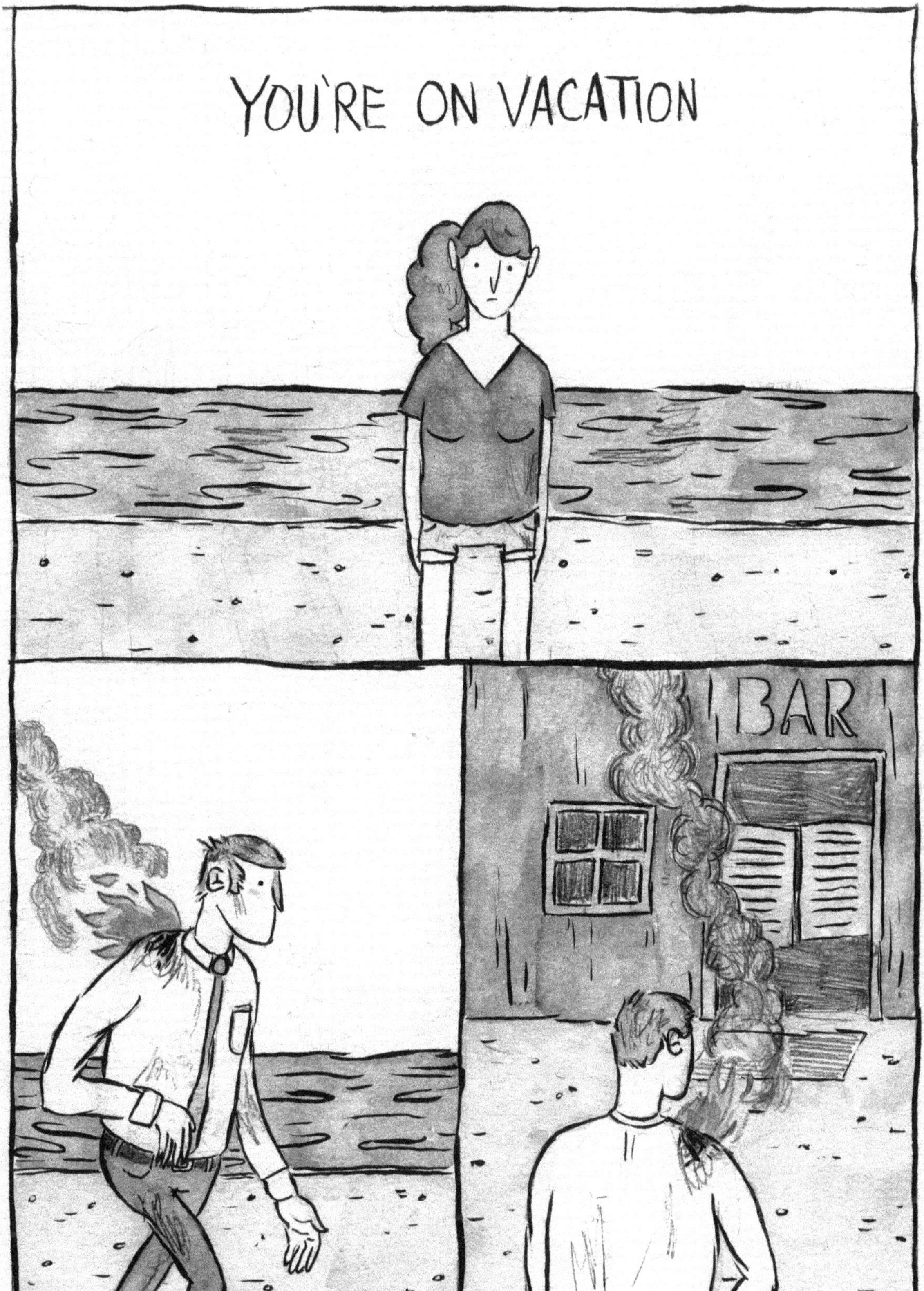
YOU'RE ON VACATION
BAR

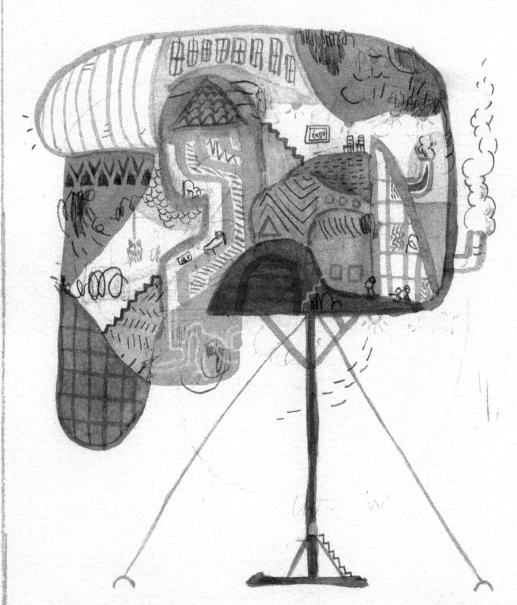

THE HOUSE IS THE SKIN OF THE MACHINE.
YOU MAKE A MISTAKE IN THE ENGINE ROOM.
MIST WRECKS THE MOUTHING PLATFORM. THE
UPPER HALLWAY GOES CROOKED. YOUR PART-
NER PERFORMS YOUR DEATH, REPEATEDLY, CO-
LLAPSING IN THE LIVING ROOM.

A CHILD OF INDETERMINATE AGE ROAMS THE
CORRIDORS. YOUR REQUEST FOR A DEFERRAL
IS MET WITH WHISPERED SQUAWING - A DEPAR-
TURE. THE IMMUNITY MACHINE SLOWS, PUTTE-
RING. THE CUBBYHOLE'S EMPTY.   AN ACTIVE
RECTANGLE VOIDS AGAINST YOU.

THE CHAPEL ROOM BURNS INFINITELY. THE
LIGHTBULBS BURN OUT. HEAT RESHAPES YOUR
MEMORY OF THE FURNITURE. AN UNTOWARD
CONVERSATION WITH YOUR MOTHER FILLS THE
STORAGE SPACE. A COLLECTION OF IMPOSSIBLE
ORNAMENTS ABSORB THE SUFFERING.

THE WITCH'S HEALTH IS IN DECLINE. DOGS BURROW INTO THE WALLS. NESTS MUDDY THE THE SKYLIGHT. ONE OF THE DOGS, IT APPEARS, MUSCLES INTO THE CEILING ABOVE THE BEDROOM, SCRATCHING AND WHINING. SEVERAL GUESTS HAVE GONE MISSING.

A HOUSE OPERATES WITHIN THE HOUSE AUTO-
NOMOUSLY. A PSYCHOLOGICAL DIAGRAM EMER-
GES. THROUGH THE WINDOW, A SMALLER
VERSION OF YOURSELF FALLS DRAMATICALLY.
THE RUNGS OF THE TINY LADDER PULSE. THE
REFRIGERATOR HANGS OPEN. YOU FLAIL
FOR YOURSELF, IN MINIATURE.

MARVELOUS TECHNOLOGY LINES THE WA-
LLS. A STEP SEQUENCER DICTATES THE OPER-
ATION. INUMMERAL CROWDS FILTER THROUGH
THE VARIOUS HOUSING COMPARTMENTS,
HANDSHAKING CONSTANTLY. A LOW-BATTERY
JAZZ MACHINE STRAYS FROM THE PULS E.
GORGEOUSLY, CHAOS ENSUES.

THE ARMCHAIRS GLINT AND YAWN IN THE
ABDOMEN. THE FACTORY ROOM REFILLS WITH
BLOOD. SMOKE SEEPS FROM THE WINDOWS.
A CLAW-FOOTED DEVICE IMAGINES THE HOUSE
IN RETROGRADE, UNTIL IT ISN'T A HOUSE
ANYMORE, THE OCCUPANTS ERASED: A
SIMULATION FOR EXTINCTION.

Alvin Dillinger, at his home,

has been Stuck

Standing,

encouraging himself:

don't worry, Alvin, everything will turn out, everythin

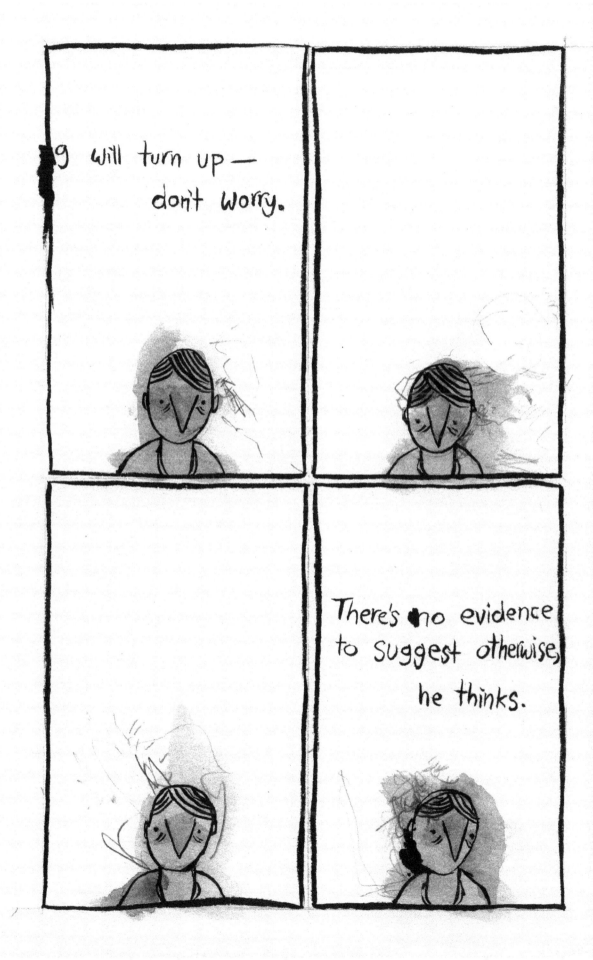

What if Conrad goes missing?

Alvin's unsure

which it is:
Whether he's been told this, or is

only now thinking it,

and so he's encouraging himself,

And though they haven't been in contact for years, and even when  they were younger they'd become mute to one another, never speaking more

than was necissary,

after Alvin tried to drown Conrad in the bathtub, and later out back in the lake near their home,  for reasons Alvin can't now remember, Alvin doesn't want to die,

and this,

Conrad's disappearance, Potentially, reminds Alvin of his Own Mortality,

and so he hopes Conrad turns up.

And so, inevitably,

Alvin too might fall

into that trap, might end up

missing

Someday,

even if his body remains, in some condition,

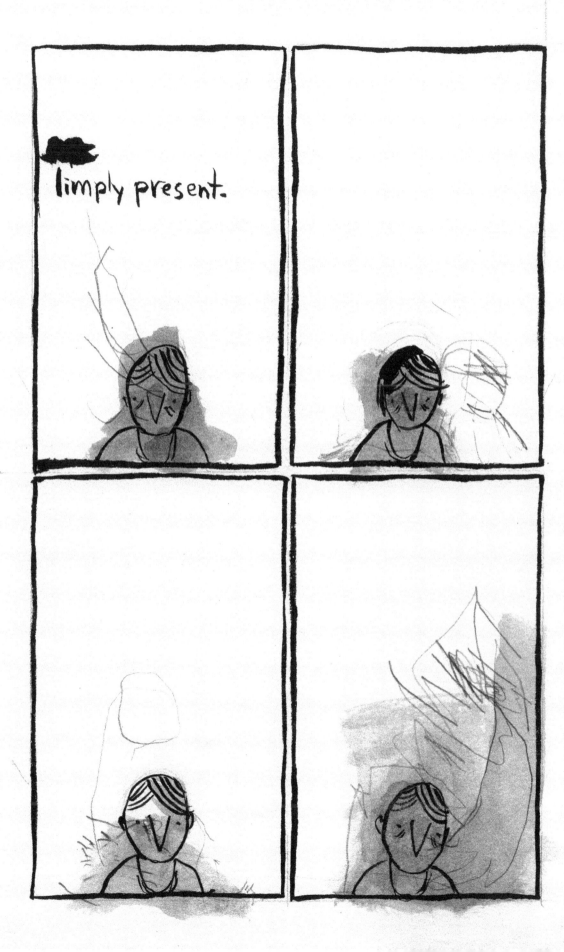

limply present.

And so he's encourag ing himself about his twin brother, Conrad,

who's been missing now for some indeterminate amount of time,

he might have been told at some point

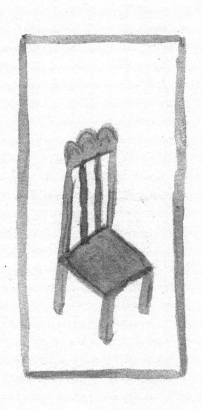

SOME NOTES ON DOMESTIC PHENOMENA

"REGARDING RECURRENT DREAD"

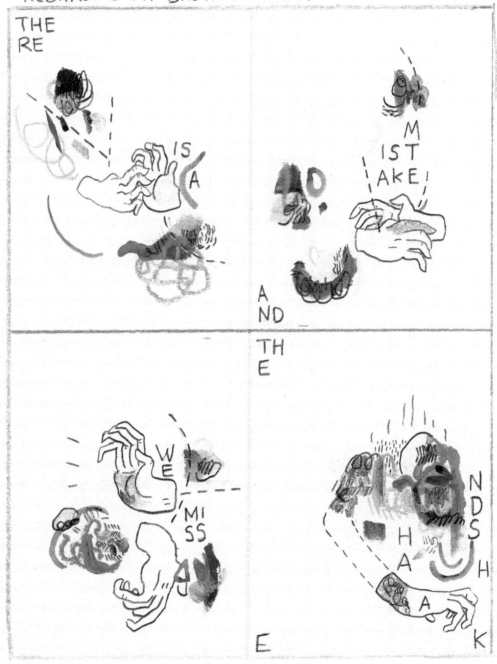

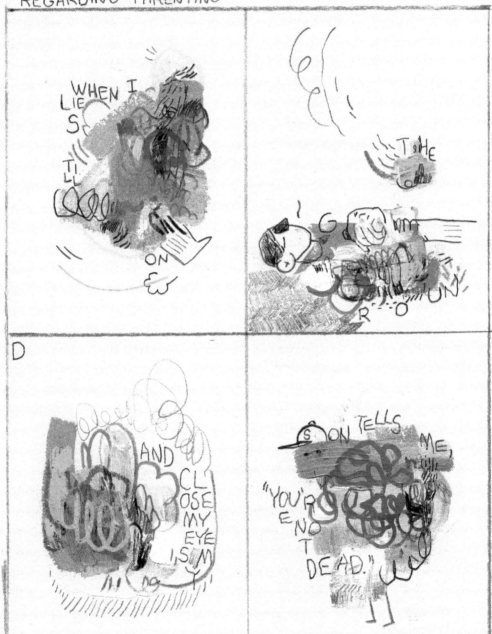

"REGARDING MY FATHER-IN-LAW"

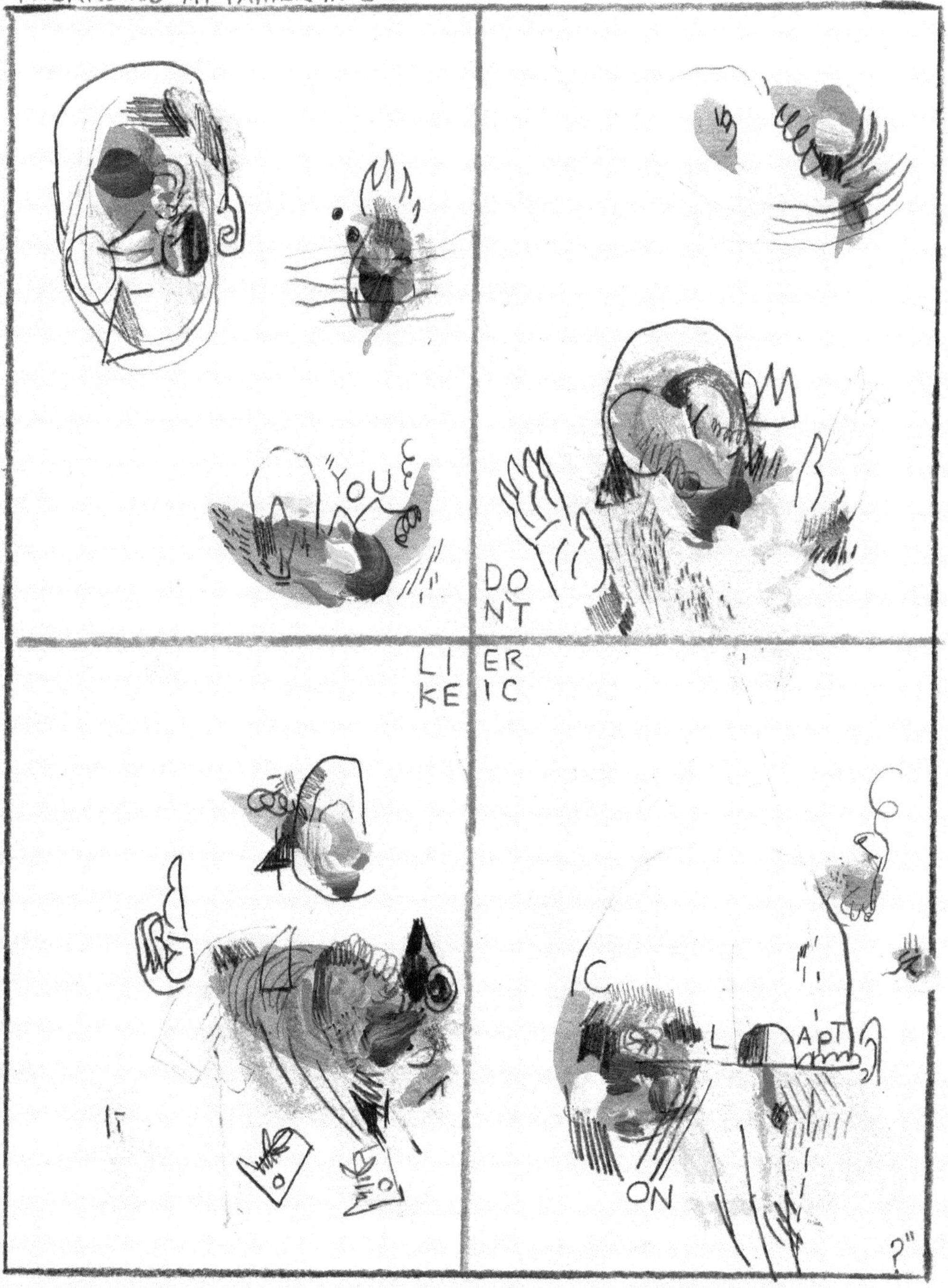

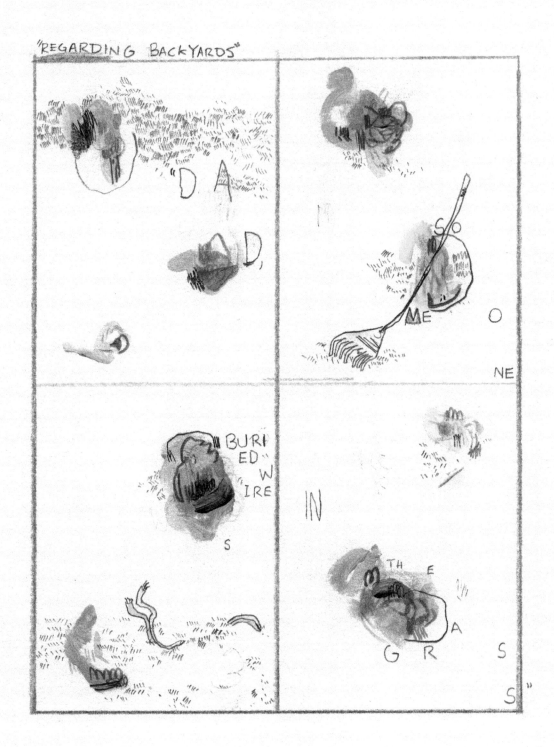

"REGARDING TV"

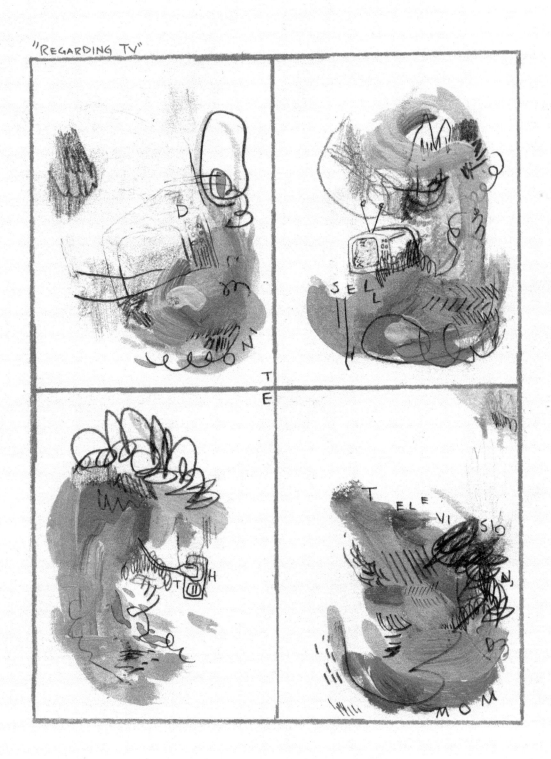

INTERLUDE

SOME NOTES ON DOMESTIC OBJECTS

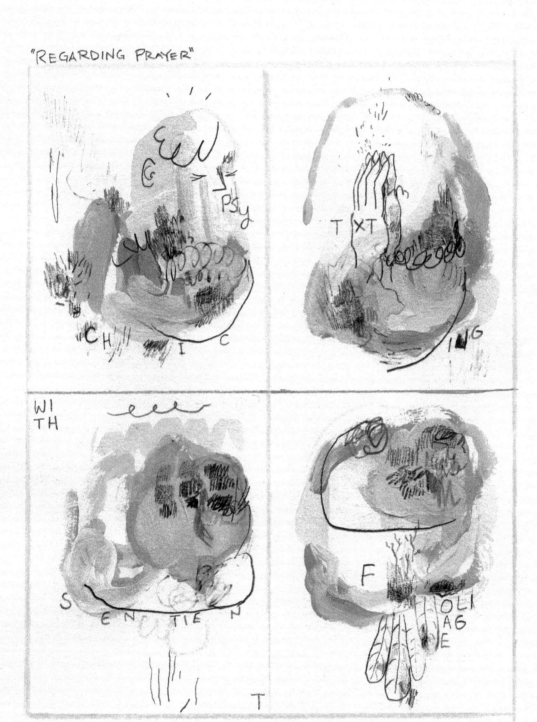

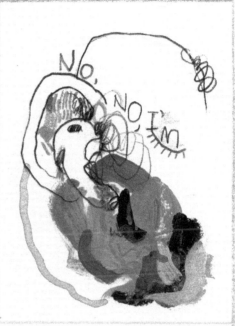

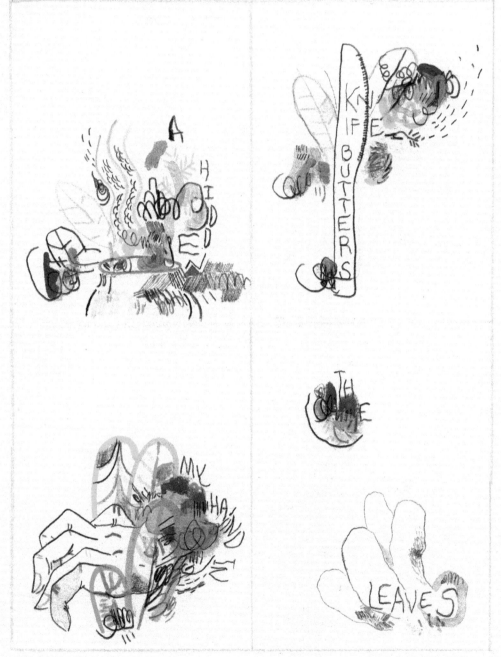

AFTER | THE PRESIDENT

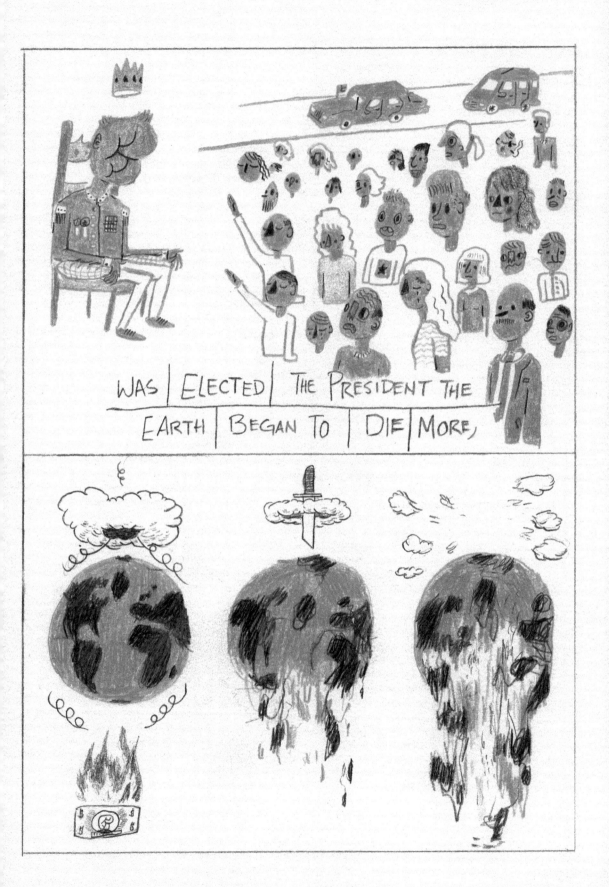

AND MORE | AND MORE | PEOPLE

BEGAN | NOTICING

OTHER | PEOPLE | WEREN'T PEOPLE | AT | ALL,

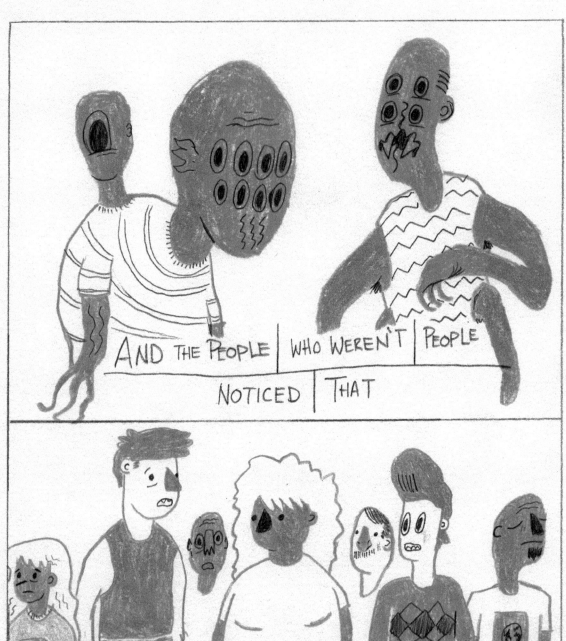

AND THE | PRESIDENT, | HAVING BEEN | ELECTED
TO | WIELD MAGIC, | COWERED | BACK IN THE

BACK | OF THE | DRESSING
ROOM

WHERE | A CAT | WHO | LOOKED LIKE
A PERSON

OR | SIMILAR TO | A | PERSON
TOYED WITH | HIS | HAIR

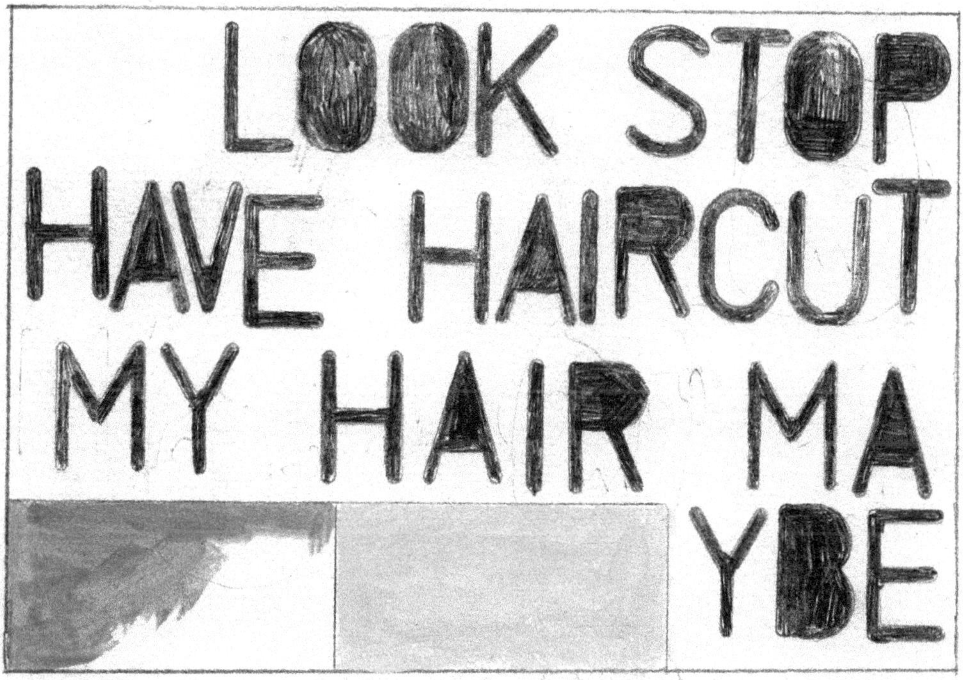
LOOK STOP
HAVE HAIRCUT
MY HAIR MA
YBE

IF NOW I BUNDLE UP
HEAD FULL HAVE FICTION UPSTAIRS
DON'T NO NOT A PROBLEM
I'M RUNNING JUST FINE TRUST
ME. AND OK MAYBE
HAIR
MAYBE OR SOMETHING LESS EVEN
THOUGH YES STILL STILL I'M STILL
GOING NO PROBLEM STILL
OR EITHER STILL
EITHER MY HAIR THOUGH
HAIR MY HAIR PLEASE

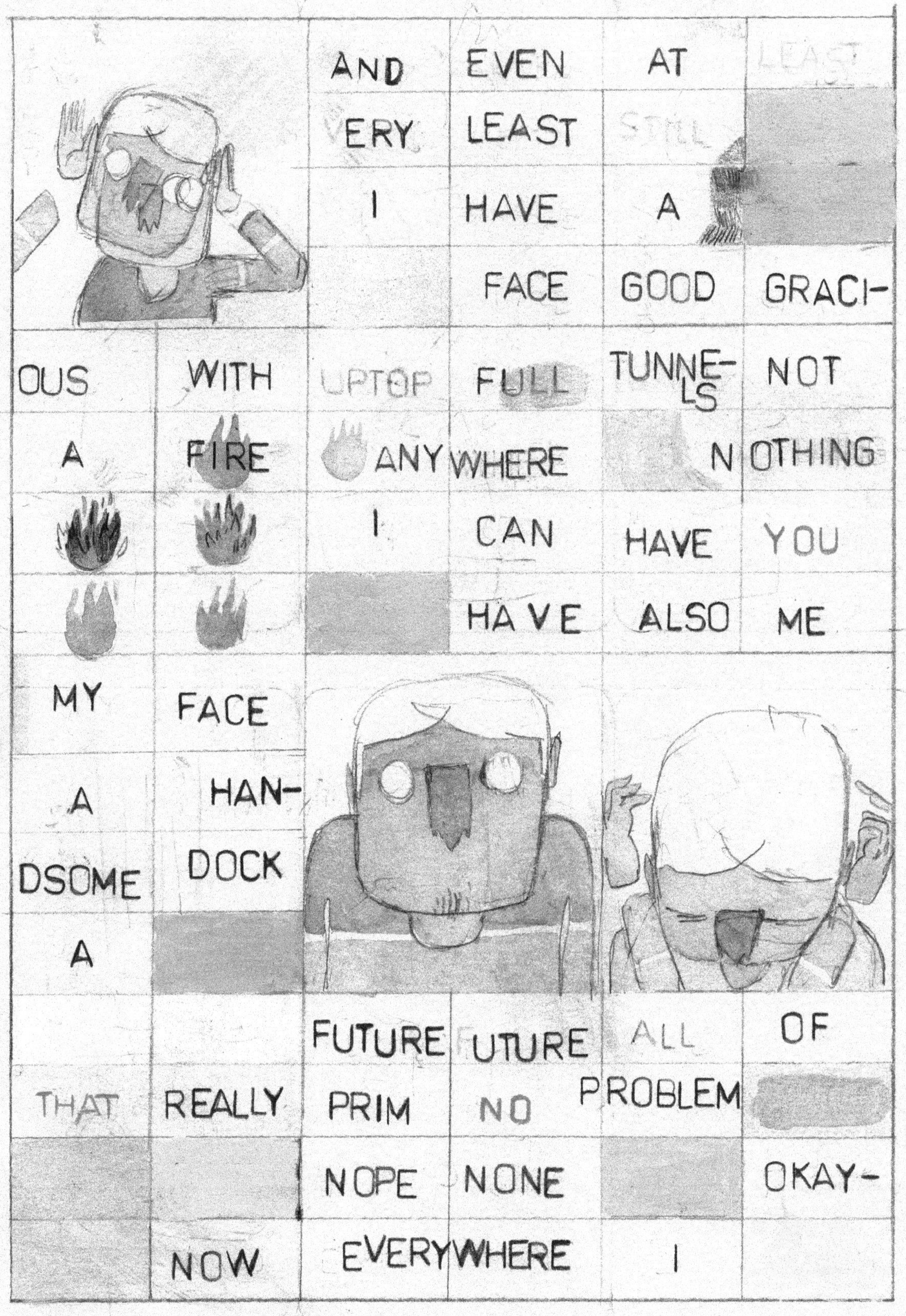

AND EVEN AT LEAST

ERY LEAST STILL

I HAVE A

FACE GOOD GRACI-

OUS WITH UPTOP FULL TUNNE-LS NOT

A FIRE ANYWHERE NOTHING

I CAN HAVE YOU

HAVE ALSO ME

MY FACE

A HAN-

DSOME DOCK

A

THAT REALLY FUTURE FUTURE ALL OF

PRIM NO PROBLEM

NOPE NONE OKAY-

NOW EVERYWHERE I

NEEDN'T DON'T NEED SO WHATEVER

I'M FINE I'M

OR MY FACE IT'S

SHIMMER— BEYOND THAT ANYWAY

MY PROJECT IS IMPORTANT WHAT'S

KEYING MY HAIR ALTER MY HAIR

AND THINKING ABOUT

COME TO THINK O.K.

YOU

KNOW

WHAT I'M

AFTER

ISN'T		OR	WELL	MAYBE	HORSE
		COMB	A	HORSE	COMB
	MY	DOG	HAIR	MY	HAIR
TOO		CUT	DOWN	SNIP	A
	BIT	TOO	REALLY		
THIS					
STEEL-TRAP	MENTION				
EVERY	BUNDLE	CAN'T			
HAVE	IT	ALL	HAVE	ALL	OF
IT.	FALL	BREAK	A	FACE	SKULL
FRACT-URE	HERE	THERE			
I	CAN	SIT	DOWN		
		EVEN	MY	FACE	MY
	GOSH	DO	YOUR	WORST	GET
WORST-ED	MY	HAIR	HERE	NOONIS H	RIG HT
	NOW	OR	FORTY-FIVE		

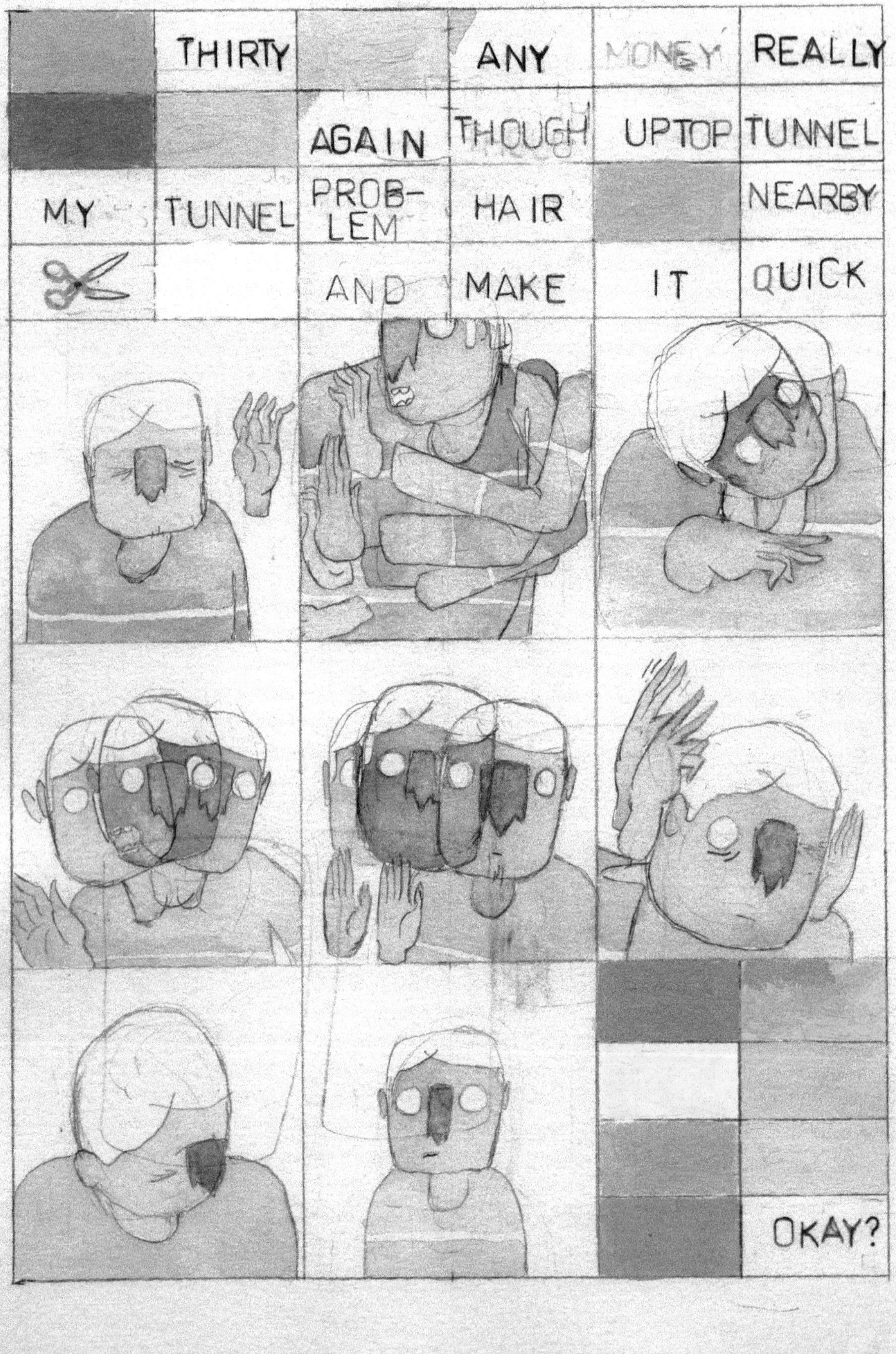
THIRTY
ANY
MONEY
REALLY
AGAIN
THOUGH
UPTOP
TUNNEL
MY
TUNNEL
PROB-
LEM
HAIR
NEARBY
AND
MAKE
IT
QUICK
OKAY?

AMBIENT DAY LABOR

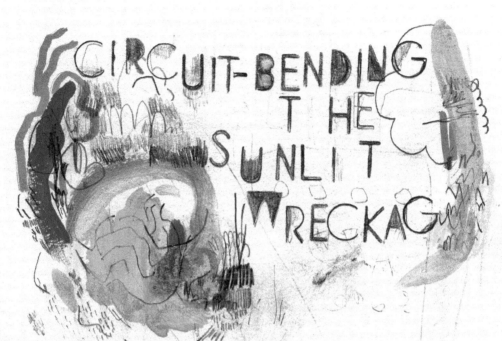

CIRCUIT-BENDING
THE
SUNLIT
WRECKAGE

OF
LATE
SUMMER
INTO

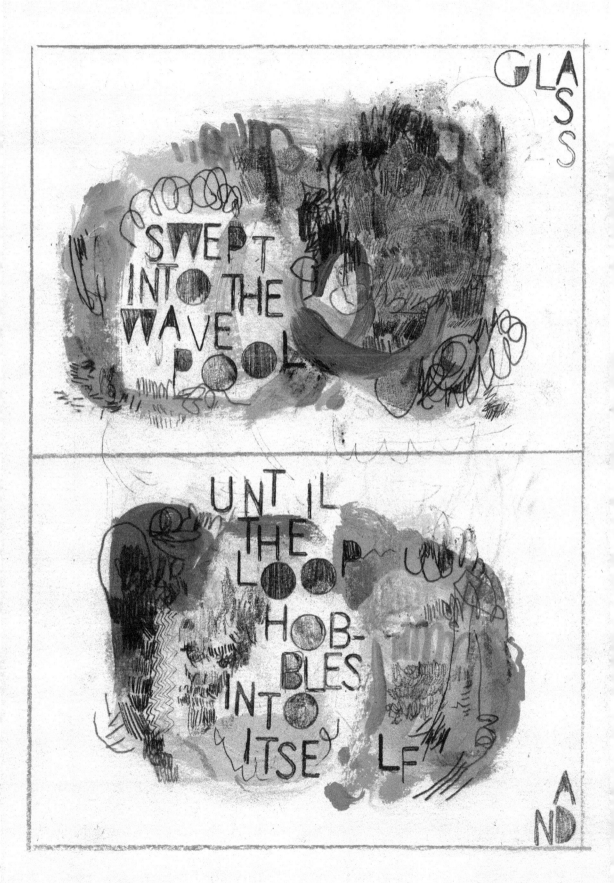

TH

E

KNE
ES

O

F

THE

ST
RU
C
TU
R
E

5

BEND

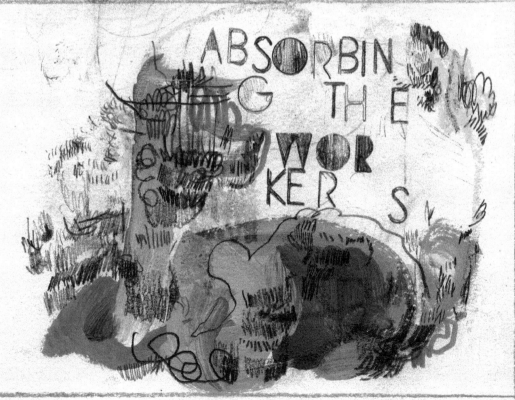

IN PITCH-SHIFTING RUBBLE

A SLOW-MOTION COLLAPSE

ST ILL,

THE LABORERS
PE RSIST

AMB
IENT

GHO
STS

W

D RO NING

AGAINST
AN AMBER
OPPRESSOR.
PAYING
IN

REVERSE

AFTER THE ANIMALS

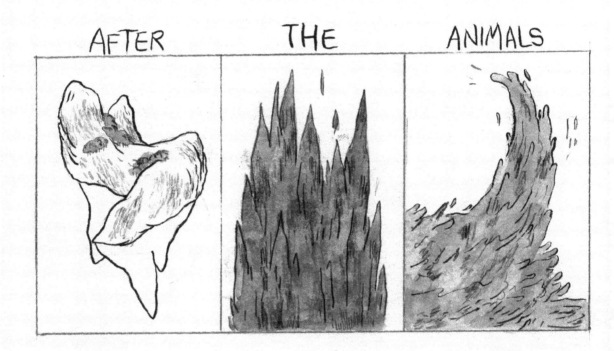

-BORED-

,

WE HACK | AT
THE LANDSCAPE,

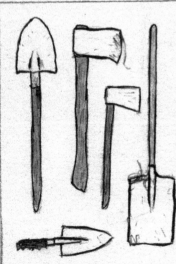

SET ENORMOUS
FIRES

AND

BUILD UNNATURAL
WATER STRUCTURE
S

WE ARE PLEASED

<u>IN</u> | THE BEGINNING

(CALL IT | FREEDOM)

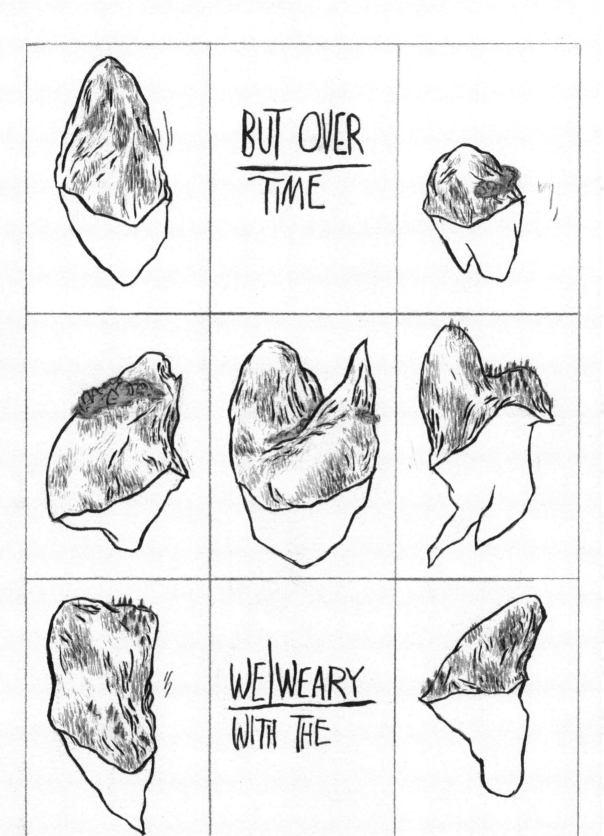

BUT OVER
TIME

WE WEARY
WITH THE

WEARY |WE
WE

WITH

WE

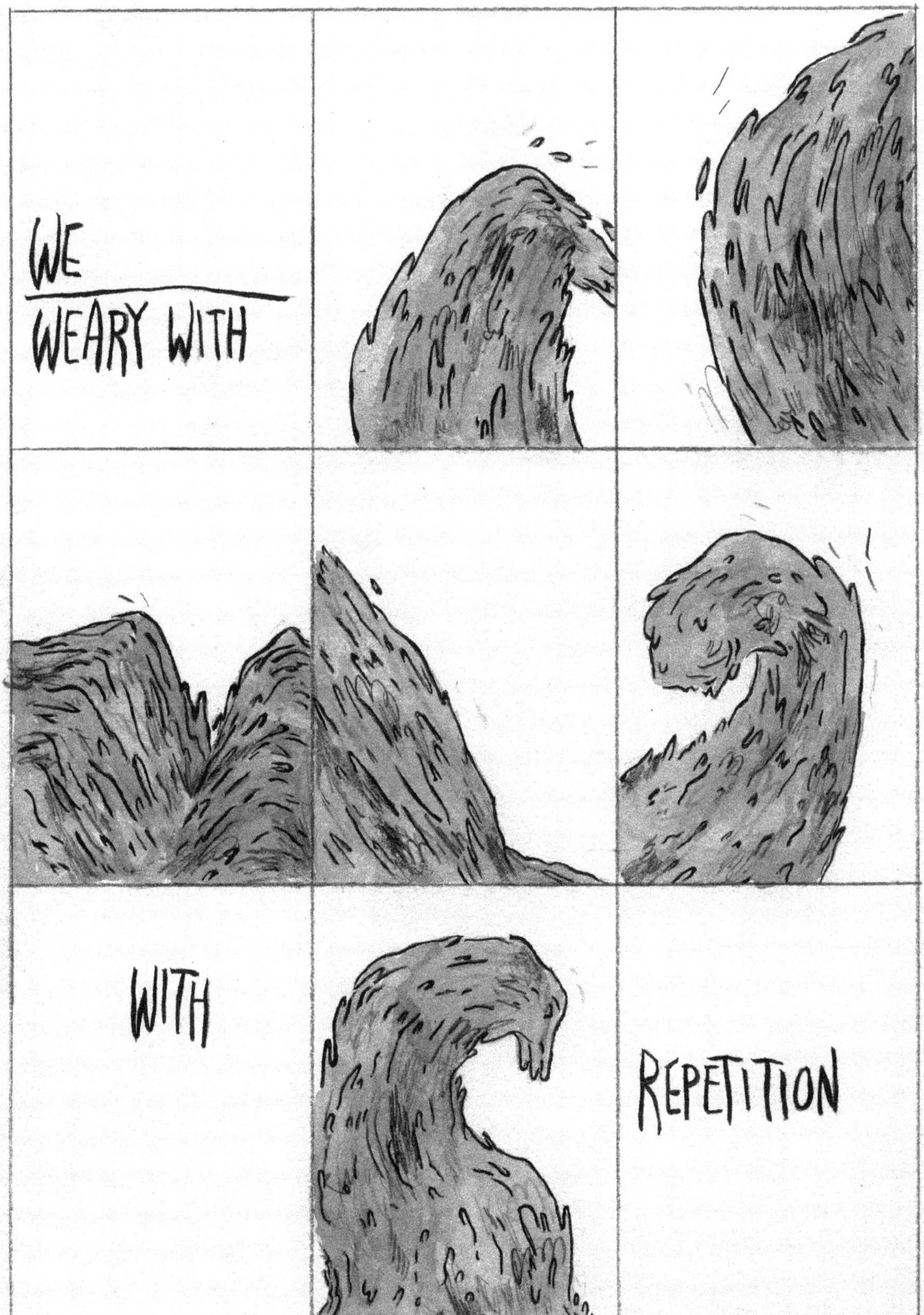
WE
WEARY WITH
WITH
REPETITION

WE SEARCH FOR
THE ANIMALST IN

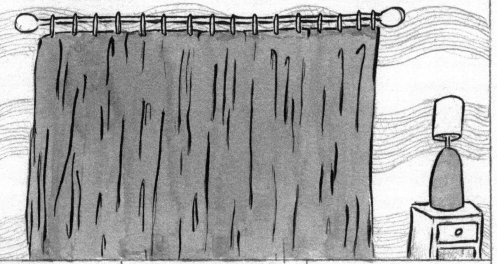

THE
PANTRY,

BEHIND
THE CURTAINS

ADRIFT IN LOSS,
WE BEGIN TO

WEAR
THEIR
ANCESTOR'S

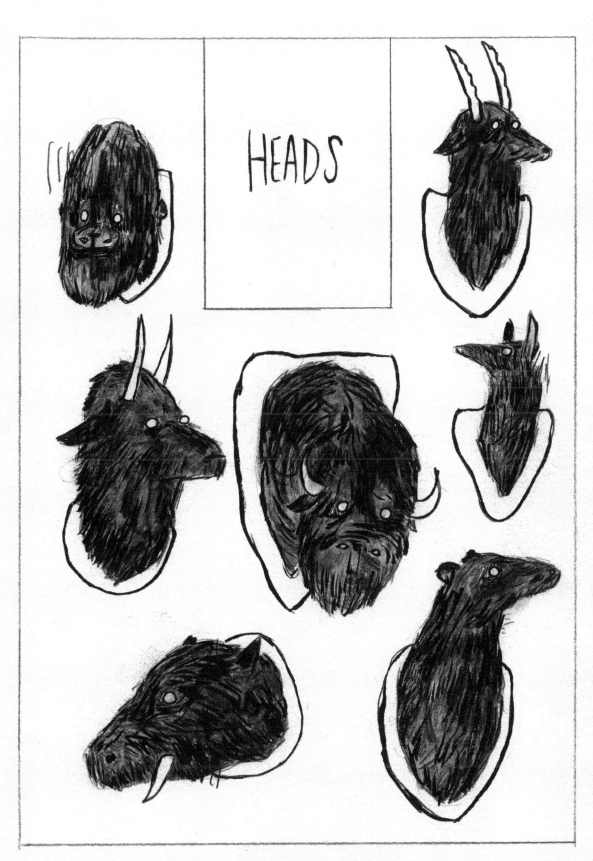

HEADS

WE ENTER THE
UNHACKED

WILDERNESS
AS ANIMALS

SLIPPING
INTO THE

LANDSCAPE'S
CLOTHING

UNTIL THE DISTANT
SMOKE

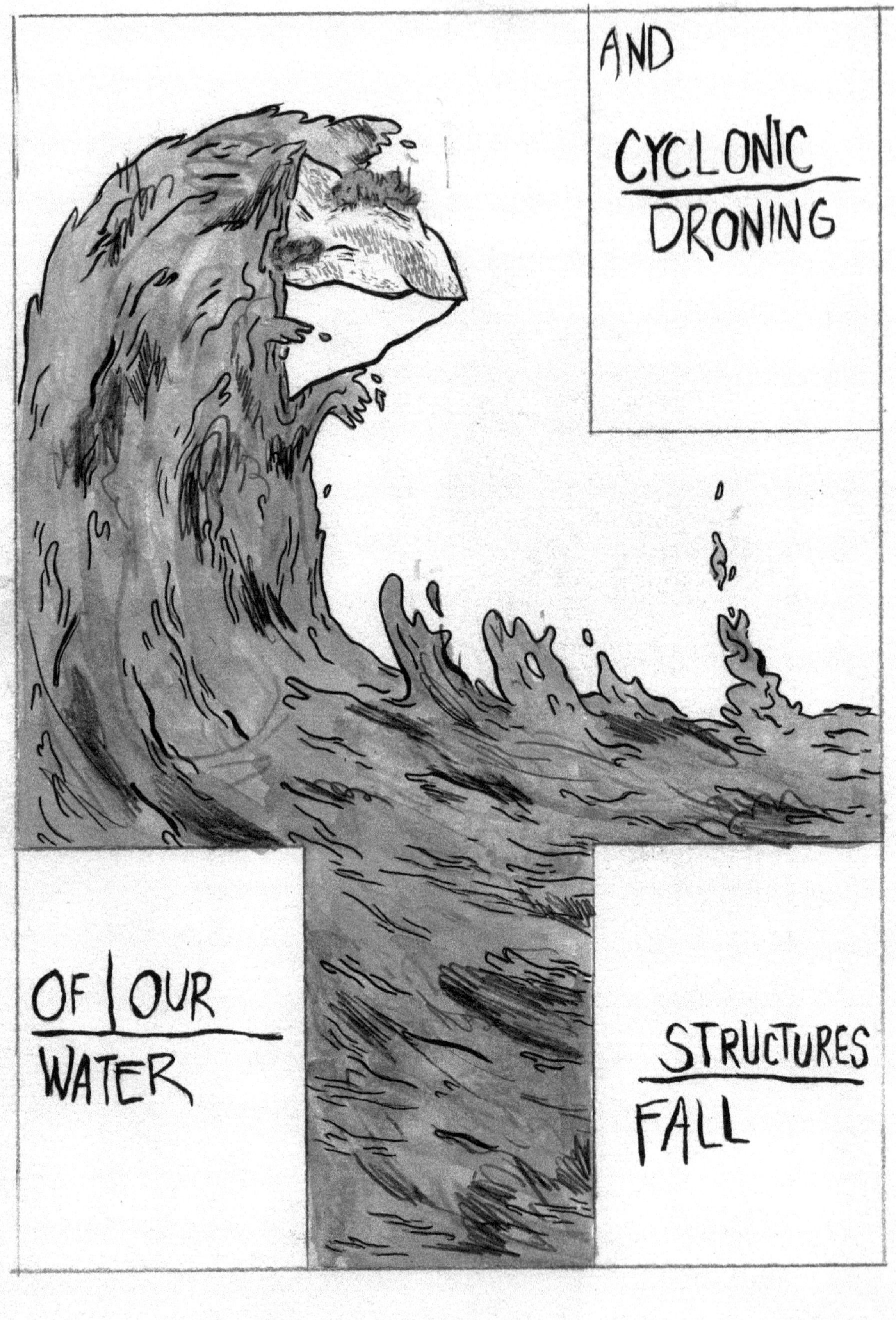
AND
CYCLONIC DRONING
OF OUR WATER
STRUCTURES FALL

BEHIND
THE HORIZON

EPILOGUE

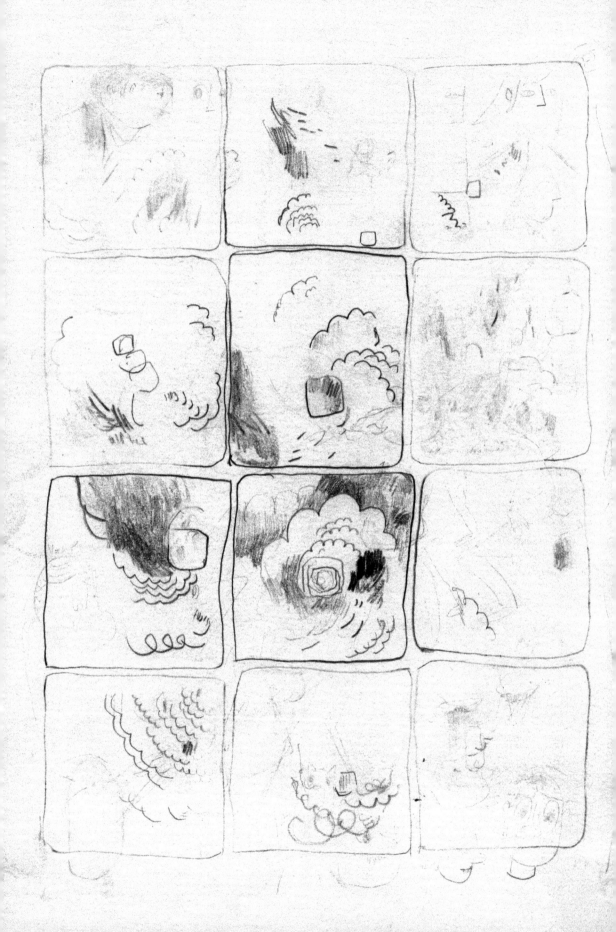

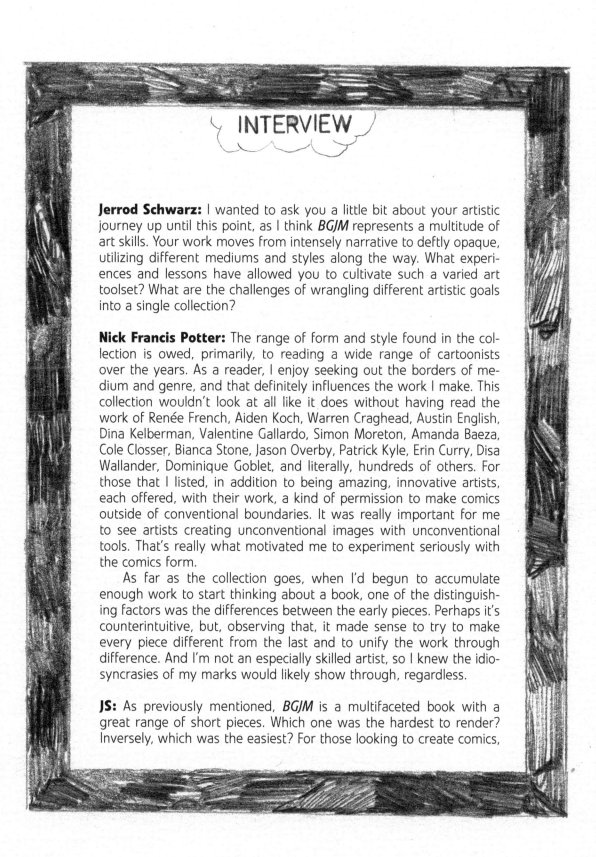

INTERVIEW

Jerrod Schwarz: I wanted to ask you a little bit about your artistic journey up until this point, as I think *BGJM* represents a multitude of art skills. Your work moves from intensely narrative to deftly opaque, utilizing different mediums and styles along the way. What experiences and lessons have allowed you to cultivate such a varied art toolset? What are the challenges of wrangling different artistic goals into a single collection?

Nick Francis Potter: The range of form and style found in the collection is owed, primarily, to reading a wide range of cartoonists over the years. As a reader, I enjoy seeking out the borders of medium and genre, and that definitely influences the work I make. This collection wouldn't look at all like it does without having read the work of Renée French, Aiden Koch, Warren Craghead, Austin English, Dina Kelberman, Valentine Gallardo, Simon Moreton, Amanda Baeza, Cole Closser, Bianca Stone, Jason Overby, Patrick Kyle, Erin Curry, Disa Wallander, Dominique Goblet, and literally, hundreds of others. For those that I listed, in addition to being amazing, innovative artists, each offered, with their work, a kind of permission to make comics outside of conventional boundaries. It was really important for me to see artists creating unconventional images with unconventional tools. That's really what motivated me to experiment seriously with the comics form.

As far as the collection goes, when I'd begun to accumulate enough work to start thinking about a book, one of the distinguishing factors was the differences between the early pieces. Perhaps it's counterintuitive, but, observing that, it made sense to try to make every piece different from the last and to unify the work through difference. And I'm not an especially skilled artist, so I knew the idiosyncrasies of my marks would likely show through, regardless.

JS: As previously mentioned, *BGJM* is a multifaceted book with a great range of short pieces. Which one was the hardest to render? Inversely, which was the easiest? For those looking to create comics,

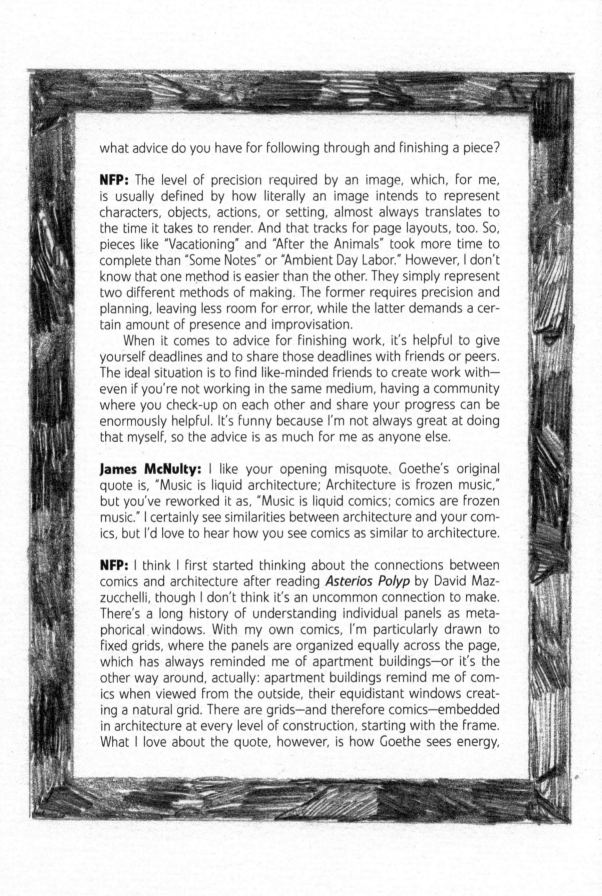

what advice do you have for following through and finishing a piece?

NFP: The level of precision required by an image, which, for me, is usually defined by how literally an image intends to represent characters, objects, actions, or setting, almost always translates to the time it takes to render. And that tracks for page layouts, too. So, pieces like "Vacationing" and "After the Animals" took more time to complete than "Some Notes" or "Ambient Day Labor." However, I don't know that one method is easier than the other. They simply represent two different methods of making. The former requires precision and planning, leaving less room for error, while the latter demands a certain amount of presence and improvisation.

When it comes to advice for finishing work, it's helpful to give yourself deadlines and to share those deadlines with friends or peers. The ideal situation is to find like-minded friends to create work with—even if you're not working in the same medium, having a community where you check-up on each other and share your progress can be enormously helpful. It's funny because I'm not always great at doing that myself, so the advice is as much for me as anyone else.

James McNulty: I like your opening misquote. Goethe's original quote is, "Music is liquid architecture; Architecture is frozen music," but you've reworked it as, "Music is liquid comics; comics are frozen music." I certainly see similarities between architecture and your comics, but I'd love to hear how you see comics as similar to architecture.

NFP: I think I first started thinking about the connections between comics and architecture after reading *Asterios Polyp* by David Mazzucchelli, though I don't think it's an uncommon connection to make. There's a long history of understanding individual panels as metaphorical windows. With my own comics, I'm particularly drawn to fixed grids, where the panels are organized equally across the page, which has always reminded me of apartment buildings—or it's the other way around, actually: apartment buildings remind me of comics when viewed from the outside, their equidistant windows creating a natural grid. There are grids—and therefore comics—embedded in architecture at every level of construction, starting with the frame. What I love about the quote, however, is how Goethe sees energy,

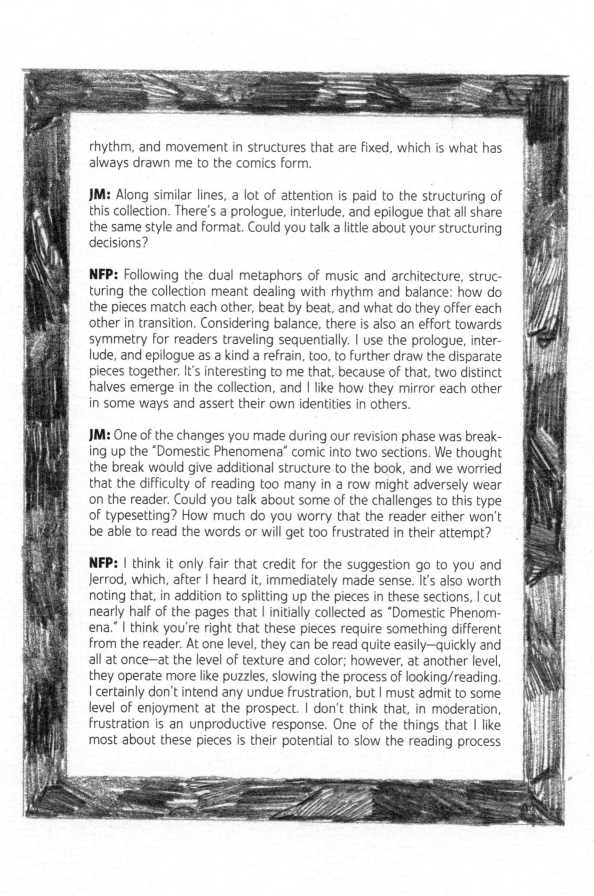

rhythm, and movement in structures that are fixed, which is what has always drawn me to the comics form.

JM: Along similar lines, a lot of attention is paid to the structuring of this collection. There's a prologue, interlude, and epilogue that all share the same style and format. Could you talk a little about your structuring decisions?

NFP: Following the dual metaphors of music and architecture, structuring the collection meant dealing with rhythm and balance: how do the pieces match each other, beat by beat, and what do they offer each other in transition. Considering balance, there is also an effort towards symmetry for readers traveling sequentially. I use the prologue, interlude, and epilogue as a kind a refrain, too, to further draw the disparate pieces together. It's interesting to me that, because of that, two distinct halves emerge in the collection, and I like how they mirror each other in some ways and assert their own identities in others.

JM: One of the changes you made during our revision phase was breaking up the "Domestic Phenomena" comic into two sections. We thought the break would give additional structure to the book, and we worried that the difficulty of reading too many in a row might adversely wear on the reader. Could you talk about some of the challenges to this type of typesetting? How much do you worry that the reader either won't be able to read the words or will get too frustrated in their attempt?

NFP: I think it only fair that credit for the suggestion go to you and Jerrod, which, after I heard it, immediately made sense. It's also worth noting that, in addition to splitting up the pieces in these sections, I cut nearly half of the pages that I initially collected as "Domestic Phenomena." I think you're right that these pieces require something different from the reader. At one level, they can be read quite easily—quickly and all at once—at the level of texture and color; however, at another level, they operate more like puzzles, slowing the process of looking/reading. I certainly don't intend any undue frustration, but I must admit to some level of enjoyment at the prospect. I don't think that, in moderation, frustration is an unproductive response. One of the things that I like most about these pieces is their potential to slow the reading process

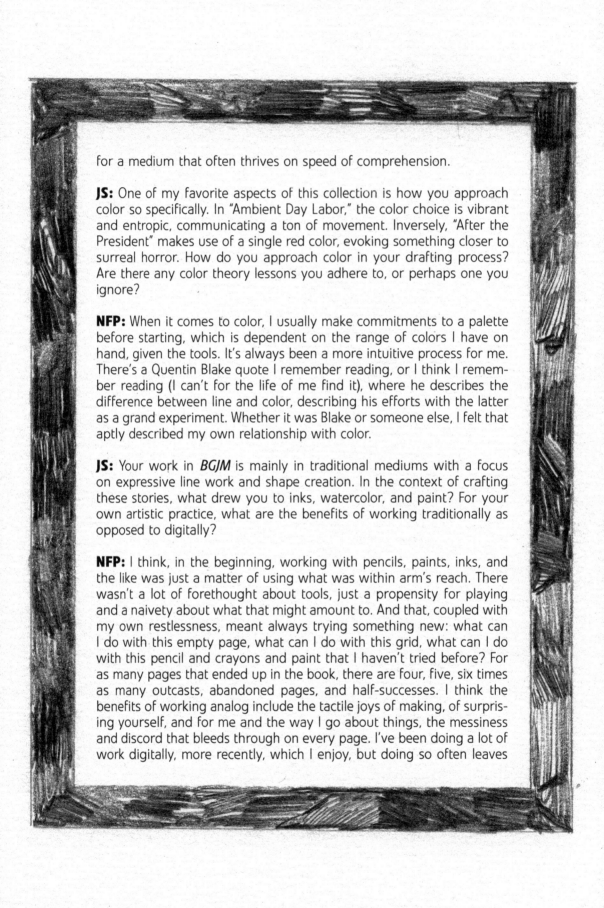

for a medium that often thrives on speed of comprehension.

JS: One of my favorite aspects of this collection is how you approach color so specifically. In "Ambient Day Labor," the color choice is vibrant and entropic, communicating a ton of movement. Inversely, "After the President" makes use of a single red color, evoking something closer to surreal horror. How do you approach color in your drafting process? Are there any color theory lessons you adhere to, or perhaps one you ignore?

NFP: When it comes to color, I usually make commitments to a palette before starting, which is dependent on the range of colors I have on hand, given the tools. It's always been a more intuitive process for me. There's a Quentin Blake quote I remember reading, or I think I remember reading (I can't for the life of me find it), where he describes the difference between line and color, describing his efforts with the latter as a grand experiment. Whether it was Blake or someone else, I felt that aptly described my own relationship with color.

JS: Your work in *BGJM* is mainly in traditional mediums with a focus on expressive line work and shape creation. In the context of crafting these stories, what drew you to inks, watercolor, and paint? For your own artistic practice, what are the benefits of working traditionally as opposed to digitally?

NFP: I think, in the beginning, working with pencils, paints, inks, and the like was just a matter of using what was within arm's reach. There wasn't a lot of forethought about tools, just a propensity for playing and a naivety about what that might amount to. And that, coupled with my own restlessness, meant always trying something new: what can I do with this empty page, what can I do with this grid, what can I do with this pencil and crayons and paint that I haven't tried before? For as many pages that ended up in the book, there are four, five, six times as many outcasts, abandoned pages, and half-successes. I think the benefits of working analog include the tactile joys of making, of surprising yourself, and for me and the way I go about things, the messiness and discord that bleeds through on every page. I've been doing a lot of work digitally, more recently, which I enjoy, but doing so often leaves me overly precious about the marks I make, trying to perfect lines and such, which is ridiculous, because I've never drawn a perfect line in my life. Working analog means indulging your flaws and celebrating them.

JS: How do you approach paneling? In your comics there is a diversity of panel structures, but the stories still feel unified and cohesive. Is paneling an intuitive process, or something more wrought?

NFP: I often begin a piece by setting the parameters for the grid first, which sets the tone for the kind of pacing and rhythm I can achieve. The paneling is the rhythm that keeps the whole thing from flying off the rails. This is particularly true for the more abstract pieces in the collection. Having a fixed grid really helps when thinking about how to transition from one panel to the next. The fixed grid is even present in some of the weirder structures, like "Look Stop Have Haircut My Hair Maybe," which, at its core, is a 3x4 grid, but with the majority of panels subdivided into 2x4 grids that allows me to break down the text, word by word. I start with a specific grid and then introduced variations based on the needs of the text or images.

JM: Many of these comics are subtly political, but "After the President" is most starkly so. Could you talk about how politics influenced these comics?

NFP: With "After the President," writing and drawing felt urgent. I didn't know quite what to do in response to the 2016 election, but I'd seen some of my poet friends talking about inauguration poems, and so that comic was born out of that moment. When it comes to the rest of my work, I don't really consider them more or less political than "After the President." They all represent decisions, conscious and unconscious, that have political implications, anxieties, and blind spots.

JS: I love the way you draw face and bodies. The forms are assured and consistent, with focal features that communicate just as much as dialogue or narration (Alvin's strong nose shape is a favorite). From your own perspective, what is crucial to express when drawing faces and bodies? Do these goals change within the context of some of your more abstract pieces?

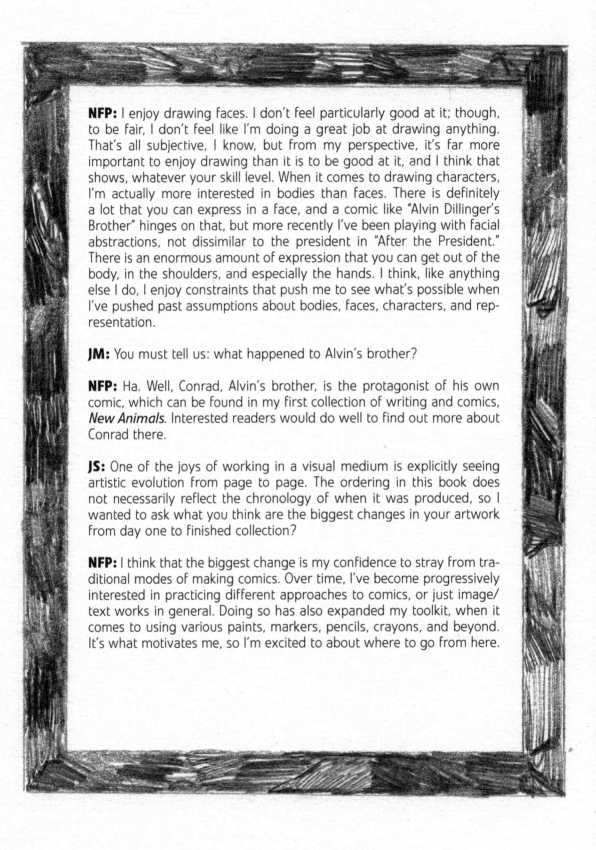

NFP: I enjoy drawing faces. I don't feel particularly good at it; though, to be fair, I don't feel like I'm doing a great job at drawing anything. That's all subjective, I know, but from my perspective, it's far more important to enjoy drawing than it is to be good at it, and I think that shows, whatever your skill level. When it comes to drawing characters, I'm actually more interested in bodies than faces. There is definitely a lot that you can express in a face, and a comic like "Alvin Dillinger's Brother" hinges on that, but more recently I've been playing with facial abstractions, not dissimilar to the president in "After the President." There is an enormous amount of expression that you can get out of the body, in the shoulders, and especially the hands. I think, like anything else I do, I enjoy constraints that push me to see what's possible when I've pushed past assumptions about bodies, faces, characters, and representation.

JM: You must tell us: what happened to Alvin's brother?

NFP: Ha. Well, Conrad, Alvin's brother, is the protagonist of his own comic, which can be found in my first collection of writing and comics, *New Animals*. Interested readers would do well to find out more about Conrad there.

JS: One of the joys of working in a visual medium is explicitly seeing artistic evolution from page to page. The ordering in this book does not necessarily reflect the chronology of when it was produced, so I wanted to ask what you think are the biggest changes in your artwork from day one to finished collection?

NFP: I think that the biggest change is my confidence to stray from traditional modes of making comics. Over time, I've become progressively interested in practicing different approaches to comics, or just image/text works in general. Doing so has also expanded my toolkit, when it comes to using various paints, markers, pencils, crayons, and beyond. It's what motivates me, so I'm excited to about where to go from here.

ACKNOWLEDGEMENTS

PROLOGUE FIRST APPEARED IN DRIFTWOOD PRESS.

VACATIONING FIRST APPEARED AS A PROSE POEM IN THE COMMENTS SECTION OF HTML GIANT. IT FIRST APPEARED AS A COMIC IN DEVIL'S LAKE. IT WAS REDRAWN FOR THIS BOOK.

ALVIN DILLINGER'S BROTHER FIRST APPEARED IN PANK MAGAZINE.

SOME SOME NOTES PREVIOUSLY APPEARED IN BIG OTHER, JUKED MAGAZINE, AND ENTROPY MAGAZINE.

LOOK STOP HAVE HAIRCUT MY HAIR MAYBE FIRST APPEARED IN HORSE LESS REVIEW, ALBEIT IN A DIFFERENT FORM. IN ITS CURRENT FORM IT WAS FIRST PUBLISHED IN ENTROPY MAG.

AMBIENT DAY LABOR FIRST APPEARED IN BIRDFEAST MAGAZINE.

AFTER THE ANIMALS FIRST APPEARED IN HEAVY FEATHER REVIEW.

MANY, MANY THANKS TO THE VARIOUS
EDITORS WHO SUPPORTED, AT DIFFERENT
STAGES, THE WORK IN THIS COLLECTION,
WITH PARTICULAR GRATITUDE TO JAMES
MCNULTY, JERROD SCHWARZ, KEITH
MCCLEARY, JOHN MADERA, JEN TYNES,
ROWAN HISAYO BUCHANAN, ROXANE GAY,
JESSICA POLI, AND JASON TEAL. ADDITION-
AL THANKS TO KATHRYN NUERNBERGER,
NATANYA ANN PULLEY, NATHAN HAUKE,
SAM CHENEY, TANYA MCQUEEN, TRUDY
LEWIS, ANDY HOBEREK, ELISA GLICK,
AND KRISTIN SCHWAIN. BUT MOSTLY
THANKS TO ERIN.

NICK FRANCIS POTTER IS THE AUTHOR
OF <u>NEW ANIMALS</u> (SUBITO PRESS) AND
<u>STATIC GIFS</u> (GREYING GHOST). HIS
WORK HAS APPEARED IN DIAGRAM,
NINTH LETTER, SOLRAD, AND ELSEWHERE.
HE IS THE COMICS EDITOR FOR ANOMALY.

Printed in the USA
CPSIA information can be obtained
at www.ICGtesting.com
LVHW061933151223
766520LV00033B/2036